A Teddy Hors...

Night

Teddy Horsley feels safe at nig...

Based on Psalm 91

by Leslie J Francis and Nicola M Slee
Pictures by Laura Cooper

The Bear facts:

The Teddy Horsley Bible Series is designed to build bridges between the young child's day-to-day experiences of the world and major biblical themes and stories

Both authors work in church-related institutions of education. Nicola Slee is a freelance writer and adult educator based at Queen's College, Birmingham. Lesl Francis is Director of the Welsh National Centre for Religious Education and Professor of Practical Theology, University of Wales, Bangor. The illustrator, Laur Cooper, is a teacher and artist.

The Teddy Horsley Series is a result of extensive research into the religious development of young children, and the authors' and illustrator's wide experienc of educational work in schools and churches.

Published by:
National Christian Education Council
1020 Bristol Road
Selly Oak
Birmingham B29 6LB

British Library Cataloguing in Publication Data:
A catalogue record for this book is available from the British Library.

Text © Leslie J Francis and Nicola M Slee 1990
Illustrations © Laura Cooper 1994

Unless otherwise stated, quotations from the Bible are from the Good News Bible, published by the Bible Societies/Colli © American Bible Society, New York, 1966, 1971, 1976.

First published 1990
ISBN 0-7197-0845-1

Reprinted 1994, 1999
Printed in the UK (By Halcyon)

Night has come and Teddy Horsley is going to bed.

He pushes open his bedroom door to peep inside.

Then he sees something stir in the corner and dark shadows play on the walls.

When Mr and Mrs Henry switch on the lamp
the shadows disappear

and Teddy Horsley sees the sleepy cat stretch in the corner.

He picks up his toys to put them in the cupboard.

Then he sees something hiding under the bed.

When Mr and Mrs Henry lift up the bedspread
Teddy Horsley laughs at his slippers lying there.

Teddy Horsley feels safe because Mr and Mrs Henry are with him in his bedroom.

He folds up his clothes to put them on the table.

Then he feels something move behind the curtains.

When he pulls the curtains back Teddy Horsley finds the window open

and the cold night breeze is blowing in.

He peers through the window to look at the black night outside.

Then he hears frightening noises echo through the darkness.

He waves to the tawny owl hooting "good night".

Teddy Horsley feels safe because Mr and Mrs Henry
are with him in the house.

Night has come and Teddy Horsley turns off the light.

He still sees shadows playing on the wall, but he is not afraid.

He still feels movement behind the curtain,
but he is not afraid.

He still hears noises echo through the darkness, but he is not afraid.

Teddy Horsley feels safe because the Lord is with him through the night.

In *Night Time*, Teddy Horsley's experience of overcoming fears of the dark brings alive the confidence of Psalm 91:

The LORD will cover you with his wings;
you will be safe in his care;
his faithfulness will protect and defend you.
You need not fear any dangers at night
or sudden attacks during the day
or the plagues that strike in the dark
or the evils that kill in daylight.

You have made the LORD your defender,
the Most High your protector,
and so no disaster will strike you,
no violence will come near your home.
God will put his angels in charge of you
to protect you wherever you go.

Psalm 91.4–6, 9–11

The following questions suggest further ways of developing the links between the young child's experience, the story and the Bible passage.

Talk about going to bed:
    How do you get ready for bed?
    Who helps you get ready for bed?
    What things do you like to have near you at night?
    Who do you like to have near you in the house when you go to bed?

Talk about the story:
    What sights did Teddy Horsley see when he opened his bedroom door?
    What did he discover when Mr and Mrs Henry switched on the light?
    What movement did Teddy Horsley feel behind the curtains?
    What did he discover when he pulled back the curtains?
    What sounds did Teddy Horsley hear in the darkness outside?
    What did he discover when he looked harder?
    How did Teddy Horsley feel when he turned out the light?
    Why did he feel safe?

Think some more about the story:
   What else might Teddy Horsley see in his bedroom at night?
   What else might he feel in the darkness?
   What else might he hear in the street outside?

Think about the Bible passage:
   A psalm is a kind of song.
   What night-time fears are described in the psalm?
   What day-time dangers are described in the psalm?
   How does God promise to protect us from night-time fears and day-time dangers?

Titles in the *Teddy Horsley* series:

Hardback *Teddy Horsley* books:
LARGE format books with LARGE words and pictures, each containing three stories

Teddy Horsley Activity Pack:
- ❖ One *Teddy Horsley* book
- ❖ *Teddy Horsley* activity book
- ❖ *Teddy Horsley* picture card
- ❖ *Teddy Horsley* cotton tidybag
- ❖ Crayons
- ❖ Removable stickers